MW00824058

HAMAKUA HERO:
A TRUE PLANTATION STORY

STORY BY
P.Y. IWASAKI

ART BY
BERIDO

3565 HARDING AVENUE, HONOLULU, HAWAI'I 96816
808.734.7159 • WWW.BESSPRESS.COM

BESS PRESS
First Printing 2010
Second Printing 2011

Library of Congress Cataloging-in-publication data

Iwasaki, Patsy.
  Hamakua hero: a true plantation
story / Patsy Iwasaki and Berido.
      p.   cm.
  Includes illustrations.
ISBN-13: 978-157306-321-0
ISBN-10: 157306-3215
1. Goto, Katsu - Comic books,
strips, etc.
2. Lynching - Hawaii - Comic
books, strips, etc.
3. Japanese - Hawaii - Honokaa -
Comic books, strips, etc.
4 . Honokaa (Hawaii) - History -
Comic books, strips, etc.
5. Graphic novels.
I. Berido. II. Title.
HV6468.H3.I93 2010   364.13-dc22

Touch-Up Art, Lettering, and Editing by DOGHOUSE ILLUSTRATION
Direction by ALAN IWASAKI

First published as "HIDDEN HERO" in Japan in 2008 by Daiwa Printing Company. "HAMAKUA HERO: A TRUE PLANTA-TION STORY" is a creative work based on actual events and characters according to various sources including personal interviews with Dr. Fumiko Kaya. Portions of the narration, chronology, events, characters, and dialogue may have been altered and/or adapted in the interest of storytelling. This work is not a definitive historical summary.

Printed in the United States of America

To
Kellie and Jairus

With Love,
PYI

HAMAKUA HERO:
A TRUE PLANTATION STORY

ITEMS OF INTEREST

There are 12 "treasures" from Hawai'i's Japanese American immigrant history placed in the artwork of this book.

tsukemono (pickles) jar
bango "ID" tag
medicine
pocketwatch
geta (footwear)
oil lantern

kori wicker suitcase
kau kau (lunch) pail
daikon (radish)
bull whip
cane knife
kasa (paper umbrella)

We invite you to search for them all.
(Answers are at the back of the book.)

ALOHA. WELCOME.
TODAY, THERE ARE OVER
1 MILLION PEOPLE OF DIVERSE
CULTURES LIVING IN THRIVING
COMMUNITIES IN THE 50TH STATE
OF AMERICA. IT IS A PLACE OF
COMMERCE, TOURISM, INDUSTRY
AND TECHNOLOGY. MANY
ARE DRAWN TO THE TROPICAL
ALLURE OF PARADISE . . .
HAWAI'I.

SEKIJIRO KOBAYAKAWA

SOME THINGS NEVER CHANGE. IT WAS THE SAME MANY YEARS AGO WHEN THOUSANDS LEFT BEHIND THEIR FAMILY, FRIENDS AND HOMELANDS FOR THESE ISLANDS IN THE MIDDLE OF THE PACIFIC OCEAN. AS MANY DO TODAY, THEY WANTED TO LIVE IN PARADISE.

LET ME TELL YOU A STORY FROM LONG AGO THAT IS VERY CLOSE TO MY HEART.

TERASAKA KOKUFU VILLAGE
KANAGAWA PREFECTURE
1884

FATHER!

WHAT IS IT,
KATSU?

IN THE LATE 1880s, POOR HARVESTS AND INCREASED LAND TAXES CAUSED A
SEVERE ECONOMIC DEPRESSION IN JAPAN. BETWEEN 1883 AND 1890, 370,000
RESIDENTS LOST THEIR PROPERTY BECAUSE THEY WERE UNABLE TO PAY THEIR
TAXES. THE JAPANESE GOVERNMENT VIEWED EMIGRATION AS A FORM OF ECONOMIC
RELIEF; AND LABORERS WOULD BE ABLE TO SEND MONEY BACK TO JAPAN.

LURED BY VISIONS OF PROSPERITY, INDEPENDENCE AND ADVENTURE, MANY
JAPANESE LOOKED ACROSS THE OCEAN TO HAWAI'I AND THE AMERICAS FOR
GREENER PASTURES.

AT THE SAME TIME, THE SUGAR PLANTATION OLIGARCHY IN HAWAI'I HAD
BEEN SEEKING OUT NEW LABOR SOURCES TO FUEL THE LUCRATIVE SUGAR
INDUSTRY THAT DOMINATED THE ISLANDS. WHEN KING DAVID KALAKAUA
VISITED JAPAN IN 1881, HE EXPRESSED HIS AND THE SUGAR PLANTERS'
DESIRE FOR JAPANESE LABORERS.

IT WASN'T LONG BEFORE 26 SHIPLOADS OF LABORERS UNDER GOVERNMENT
CONTRACTS FROM JAPAN BRAVED THE CROWDED, LONG STEAMER VOYAGE TO THE
TROPICAL HAWAIIAN ISLANDS. THE FIRST WAS THE "S. S. CITY OF TOKIO" WITH
944 JAPANESE NATIONALS - 676 MEN, 158 WOMEN AND 110 CHILDREN - WHICH
ARRIVED IN HONOLULU ON FEBRUARY 8, 1885.

BY 1924, OVER 200,000 JAPANESE FROM THE COUNTRYSIDES OF HIROSHIMA,
YAMAGUCHI, KUMAMOTO, OKINAWA, AND OTHER PREFECTURES, HAD EMIGRATED TO
HAWAI'I AND TO THE U.S. THEY WERE MOSTLY FARMERS AND OFTEN SECOND OR
THIRD SONS. THEY CAME IN SEARCH OF A BETTER LIFE, HOPING TO "STRIKE
GOLD" AND CREATE NEW LIVES IN HAWAI'I, WITH SOME DREAMING OF RETURNING
TO JAPAN AS WEALTHY MEN.

6

*SHINNEN AKEMASHITE OMEDETOO 1885!

•BEST WISHES FOR A HAPPY NEW YEAR 1885!

IN JAPAN, THE NEW YEAR'S HOLIDAY WAS THE COUNTRY'S MOST CELEBRATED EVENT AND WAS HELD FROM DECEMBER 28 TO JANUARY 6

•KADOMATSU - NEW YEAR'S DECORATION MADE OF BAMBOO AND PINE

•JYUBAKO - LACQUERED BOXES USED FOR SERVING OSECHI RYORI

•OSECHI RYORI - NEW YEAR'S CELEBRATORY FOOD

DON'T FORGET. YOU AND SEKIJIRO NEED TO GO TO UNCLE'S HOUSE TO POUND *MOCHI AT DAYBREAK TOMORROW.

•MOCHI - JAPANESE RICE CAKES

SHE STILL THINKS OF ME AS A YOUNG CHILD . . .

ALMOST . . .

THERE. FINALLY DONE.

. . . THAT'S A GOOD BOY.

10

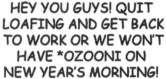 HEY YOU GUYS! QUIT LOAFING AND GET BACK TO WORK OR WE WON'T HAVE *OZOONI ON NEW YEAR'S MORNING!

*OZOONI - RICE CAKES IN BROTH WITH VEGETABLES

 YES, AUNTY! HA HA HA

 I THINK THE MOCHI'S DONE...

KATSU, ABOUT WHAT YOU SAID EARLIER. YOU'D BE A COMMON LABORER YOU KNOW.

I JUST GOT TO SEE WHAT'S OUT THERE.

IT'S JUST SOMETHING I HAVE TO DO.

THIS IS SERIOUSLY GOING TO CHANGE MY PLANS.

I THOUGHT I COULD GO OFF SOMEWHERE, SINCE YOU WERE GOING TO STAY HOME.

 YOU'LL HAVE YOUR CHANCE. I PROMISE.

I FEEL IT IN MY BLOOD.

 ALL RIGHT THEN! LET'S SEE WHAT'S IN YOUR BLOOD.

OKAY, YOU ASKED FOR IT!

11

KATSU, NOW THAT THE NEW YEAR'S HOLIDAY IS OVER...

I HAVE SOMETHING I NEED TO TALK TO YOU ABOUT.

REMEMBER MRS. NAKAYAMA FROM THE CHURCH LADIES GROUP?

SHE HAS A NIECE. LOOK, ISN'T SHE PRETTY?

SHE'S 18 YEARS OLD, VERY SMART, DID WELL IN SCHOOL AND HELPS TAKE CARE OF HER GRANDPARENTS. SHE'S A HARD WORKER AND IS NEVER SICK.

MRS. NAKAYAMA TOLD HER PARENTS THAT YOU HAVE A GOOD JOB AND YOU'RE THE OLDEST SON. YOU NEED TO START THINKING ABOUT SETTLING DOWN AND YOUR OWN *KEKKON SHIKI ...

*KEKKON SHIKI - WEDDING

12

13

MISTER, HEY MISTER!

...YOU CAN'T LEAVE... YOU'RE MY FIRST BORN SON!!

...YOU CANNOT LEAVE ME.

I'VE BEEN TELLING YOU, HERE'S YOUR ADOPTION PAPERWORK.

HUH? I'M SORRY. WHAT'S THAT?

OKAY. THIS SEEMS TO BE IN ORDER.

·ACCORDING TO JAPANESE CUSTOM AND LAW, KATSU KOBAYAKAWA WAS NOT ALLOWED TO LEAVE JAPAN AS THE FIRST SON AND HEIR OF THE KOBAYAKAWA FAMILY. TO JOIN THE KANYAKU IMIN, HE GAVE UP HIS FAMILY NAME AND ALL RIGHTS TO THE FAMILY HOME AND LAND. KATSU FILED ADOPTION PAPERS WITH MASUGORO AND HARU GOTO, WHO WERE PREPARING TO LEAVE FOR HAWAI'I.

THE FIRST IMMIGRATION SHIP, THE "S. S. CITY OF TOKIO."

IT MUST HAVE BEEN A DIFFICULT DECISION, BUT IT ALLOWED KATSU TO FOLLOW HIS DREAMS. HE WAS 23 YEARS OLD.

S. S. CITY OF TOKIO

JANUARY 1885

THE "S.S. CITY OF TOKIO,"
ARRIVED IN HONOLULU ON
FEBRUARY 8, 1885.

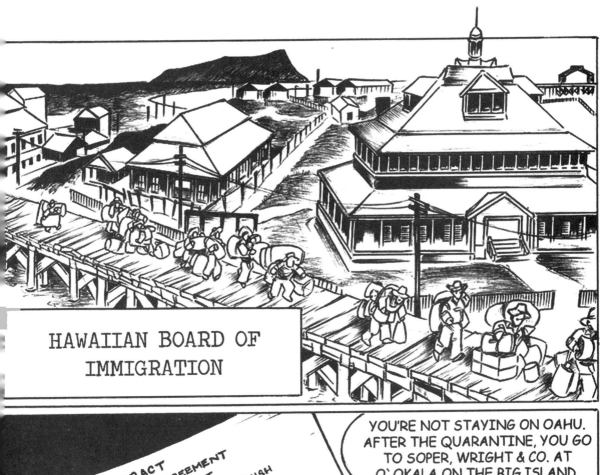

HAWAIIAN BOARD OF IMMIGRATION

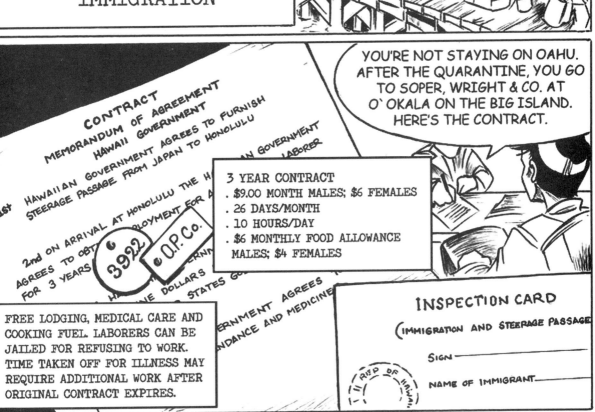

CONTRACT

MEMORANDUM OF AGREEMENT
Hawaii Government

1st Hawaiian Government agrees to furnish steerage passage from Japan to Honolulu

2nd on arrival at Honolulu the ...AN GOVERNMENT ...LABORER agrees to obt...loyment for a... for 3 years ...

YOU'RE NOT STAYING ON OAHU. AFTER THE QUARANTINE, YOU GO TO SOPER, WRIGHT & CO. AT O'OKALA ON THE BIG ISLAND. HERE'S THE CONTRACT.

3 YEAR CONTRACT
. $9.00 MONTH MALES; $6 FEMALES
. 26 DAYS/MONTH
. 10 HOURS/DAY
. $6 MONTHLY FOOD ALLOWANCE
  MALES; $4 FEMALES

FREE LODGING, MEDICAL CARE AND COOKING FUEL. LABORERS CAN BE JAILED FOR REFUSING TO WORK. TIME TAKEN OFF FOR ILLNESS MAY REQUIRE ADDITIONAL WORK AFTER ORIGINAL CONTRACT EXPIRES.

INSPECTION CARD
(IMMIGRATION AND STEERAGE PASSAGE

SIGN

NAME OF IMMIGRANT

20

·THE CONTRACTS OF THE FIRST THREE LOTS OF IMMIGRANTS STIPULATED THAT "TRAVEL TIME" TO AND FROM THE WORK SITES BE INCLUDED IN THE 10 HOUR DAY. BUT ROBERT OVEREND OF OʻOKALA PLANTATION ROUTED OUT HIS LABORERS AT DAYBREAK AND MARCHED THEM TO A WORK SITE TWO MILES WEST OF HONOKAʻA. INSTEAD OF FIELDS OF GOLD, THE JAPANESE MET HARD, DEGRADING LABOR.

IN POOR AND DANGEROUS CONDITIONS...

THIS ACCIDENT SHOULDN'T HAVE HAPPENED!

IT'S YOUR FAULT! HE WAS TOO WEAK AND YET YOU MADE HIM COME TO HAWAI`I!

IT'S YOUR FAULT! YOU WERE TOO HUNG OVER TO WATCH HIM!

CALM DOWN. I TALKED TO HIM MANY TIMES.

RIKIO WANTED TO COME TO HAWAI`I... HE KNEW THE RISKS.

HE WAS FOLLOWING HIS DREAM.

YOU'RE RIGHT, KATSU. HE WANTED TO BE HERE IN HAWAI`I...

THIS ISN'T BAD...
KINDA REMINDS
ME OF HOME.

HA HA!!

OH YEAH,
WE'VE GOT GOOD
*SAKE TOO!

*SAKE - JAPANESE RICE WINE

CONGRATULATIONS!

CONGRATULATIONS!!
A BOY!!

BORN IN MAY!
JUST IN TIME FOR
BOY'S DAY!

·THE HAWAIIAN ISLANDS
WERE ANNEXED TO THE U.S.
ON JULY 7, 1898. INFANTS
BORN AFTER THIS DATE
BECAME U.S. CITIZENS.

GOOD HUH?

25

26

27

GOTO BECAME FRIENDS WITH BUNICHIRO ONOME, AN IMMIGRATION OFFICIAL, WHO WAS RECOVERING FROM BERIBERI IN HONOKA'A AND HAD TAKEN UP COFFEE FARMING. IN FEBRUARY 1888, THE GOVERNMENT GRANTED ONOME A PERMIT TO OPEN A STORE.

NO BANKS WOULD LEND MONEY TO IMMIGRANT JAPANESE SO 11 OTHER JAPANESE MEN POOLED THEIR MONEY AND FORMED A *TANOMOSHI TO PROVIDE LOANS TO ITS MEMBERS.

*TANOMOSHI - A MUTUAL FINANCING ASSOCIATION

PLANNING TO VISIT JAPAN, ONOME TRANSFERRED THE PERMIT TO GOTO.

IN 1888, GOTO BECAME THE FIRST JAPANESE STOREKEEPER IN HONOKAʻA, HAWAIʻI.

GOTO'S GENERAL STORE CARRIED FOOD, CLOTHING, HOUSEHOLD GOODS, HARDWARE, ANIMAL SUPPLIES; ALL THE NECESSITIES.

RICE	$.05/LB.
MOCHI FLOUR	$.06/LB.
SHOYU	$3.25/BARREL
CANNED SARDINES	$1.50/DOZEN CANS
SHIITAKE DRIED MUSHROOMS	$.38/LB.
DRIED SHRIMP	$.25/LB.
NORI	$.06/LB.
DENIM PANTS	$.67
3 PIECE SUIT	$10

HE ALSO SOLD A FEW SPECIALTY ITEMS AND MERCHANDISE SUCH AS JAPANESE MEDICINE AND COSMETICS THAT MADE THE JAPANESE IMMIGRANTS FEEL CLOSER TO THEIR HOMELAND.

MOST JAPANESE MEN WANTED TO MARRY JAPANESE WOMEN, SO THE "PICTURE BRIDE" INDUSTRY FLOURISHED BETWEEN 1908 AND 1924. ABOUT 20,000 JAPANESE, OKINAWAN AND KOREAN WOMEN IMMIGRATAED TO HAWAI'I WITH ONLY A PHOTO OF THEIR HUSBANDS. MARRIAGES WERE ARRANGED THROUGH PICTURES, WITH MANY MEN SENDING PHOTOS TAKEN YEARS, EVEN DECADES, EARLIER. MANY BRIDES, OFTEN YOUNG GIRLS IN THEIR TEENS, WERE "SUPRISED." ALTHOUGH PICTURE BRIDES ARRIVED ALMOST 20 YEARS AFTER THE EVENTS TOLD IN THIS BOOK, IN THE INTEREST OF STORYTELLING, THIS IMPORTANT SEGMENT OF JAPANESE AMERICAN HISTORY IN HAWAI'I HAS BEEN INCLUDED. PICTURE BRIDES WERE ESSENTIAL TO THE SETTLING OF THE JAPANESE IMMIGRANTS IN HAWAI'I AND THE BUILDING OF COMMUNITIES.

HA HA HA HA HA

ARE YOU LOOKING FOR SOMETHING IN PARTICULAR?

HA HA
HEY! YOU HAVE JAPANESE COSMETICS AND MEDICINE !?

MY STOMACH...

IT'S BEEN UPSET SINCE THE BOAT RIDE OVER. DO YOU KNOW WHAT IT COULD BE?

34

GOTO SOON BECAME A LEADER
IN THE FLEDGLING JAPANESE COMMUNITY IN HONOKA'A.

AS THE JAPANESE LABORERS BEGAN
TO SEE THE SEVERE INJUSTICES OF
THE PLANTATION SYSTEM, THEY BANDED
TOGETHER AND, IN SMALL WAYS AT FIRST,
TRIED TO SEEK IMPROVEMENTS.

GOTO BECAME THE LIAISON BETWEEN THE
LABORERS AND PLANTATION MANAGEMENT.
HE ADVOCATED FOR IMPROVED WORKING
CONDITIONS AND WAGES. HE FACILITATED
MEDIATION AND SERVED AS THE INTERPRETER.

GOTO WAS A LABOR LEADER
FOR THE JAPANESE WORKERS

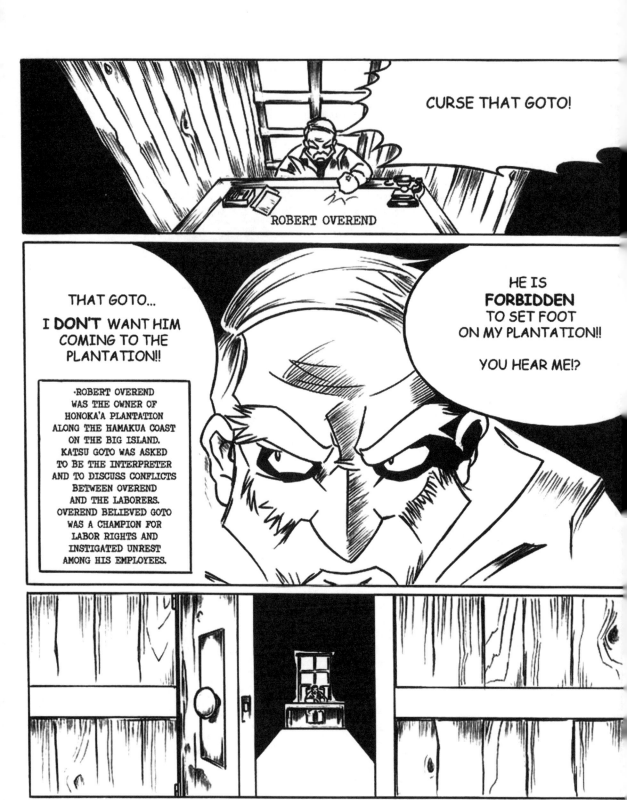

K. GOTO STORE

IN A SHORT TIME, GOTO'S GENERAL STORE PROSPERED. IT SOON BECAME A GATHERING PLACE FOR THE HONOKA'A COMMUNITY.

GOTO DID A BRISK BUSINESS - $500-$600 PER MONTH AND WAS ABLE TO HIRE A CLERK, S. ISAOKA.

THANK YOU.

WHEN HE RAN SHORT OF SUPPLIES, HE BOUGHT THEM FROM JOSEPH R. MILLS, WHO OWNED THE ONLY OTHER GENERAL STORE IN HONOKA'A, JUST YARDS FROM GOTO'S STORE.

GOTO ALSO MADE ARRANGEMENTS WITH MILLS FOR DELIVERY OF LARGE PACKAGES FROM THE HONOKA'A LANDING AT THE OCEAN FRONT. MILLS MADE ABOUT $75 FROM THE AGREEMENT.

JOSEPH R. MILLS

ROBERT OVEREND'S
PLANTATION HOUSE

SIR, I JUST HAD THE WORKERS GO OVER TO THE SITE, BUT SOME OF THEM SAID THEY WERE SICK AND COULDN'T WORK.

... THE MEN JUST WON'T GET OUT OF BED.

THOMAS STEELE

WHAT?!!

SICK, MY FOOT! IT'S A REBELLION. THAT GOTO AGAIN!

40

42

AN INVESTIGATION FOLLOWED, AND A HEARING TOOK PLACE INVOLVING THE MEN WHO SAID THEY WERE SICK AND COULDN'T WORK TWO WEEKS EARLIER. DISTRICT JUDGE FREDERICK S. LYMAN SENTENCED ONE SUSPECT TO JAIL FOR 30 DAYS. OVEREND HIRED AN ATTORNEY TO SUE THE REMAINING SUSPECTS FOR BREACH OF CONTRACT AND ABSTAINING FROM WORK.

OCTOBER 28, 1889

YOU ARE BEING FINED $20 FOR BREACH OF CONTRACT!

WHAT!?

$20! WE DON'T HAVE THAT KIND OF MONEY!

WE HAD NOTHING TO DO WITH THE FIRE! WE ONLY MAKE $9 A MONTH

AND ONLY GET $6.75!

·SAVINGS PROGRAM - 25% OF WAGES AUTOMATICALLY WENT TO THE JAPANESE CONSULATE TO BE DEPOSITED IN THE HAWAIIAN GOVERNMENT POSTAL SAVINGS AT 5% ANNUM.

YOU TWO CAN LEAVE NOW.

CALCULATE TIME LOST AND KEEP IT HANDY.

YES SIR, MR. OVEREND.

48

49

ROBERT OVEREND BELIEVED GOTO WAS BEHIND THE UNREST AMONG HIS JAPANESE LABORERS. HE HAD CURSED GOTO AND HAD FORBADE HIM ACCESS TO HONOKAʻA PLANTATION A YEAR BEFORE, WHEN HIS THREE-YEAR CONTRACT WAS FULFILLED AT NEARBY SOPER, WRIGHT & CO. ALSO KNOWN AS OʻOKALA PLANTATION. OVEREND THREATENED GOTO WITH HIS LIFE IF HE EVER CAME TO HIS EMPLOYEES' QUARTERS AT OVEREND CAMP.

IF I **EVER** SEE YOU ON MY PROPERTY TALKING TO MY WORKERS, YOU'RE A DEAD MAN.

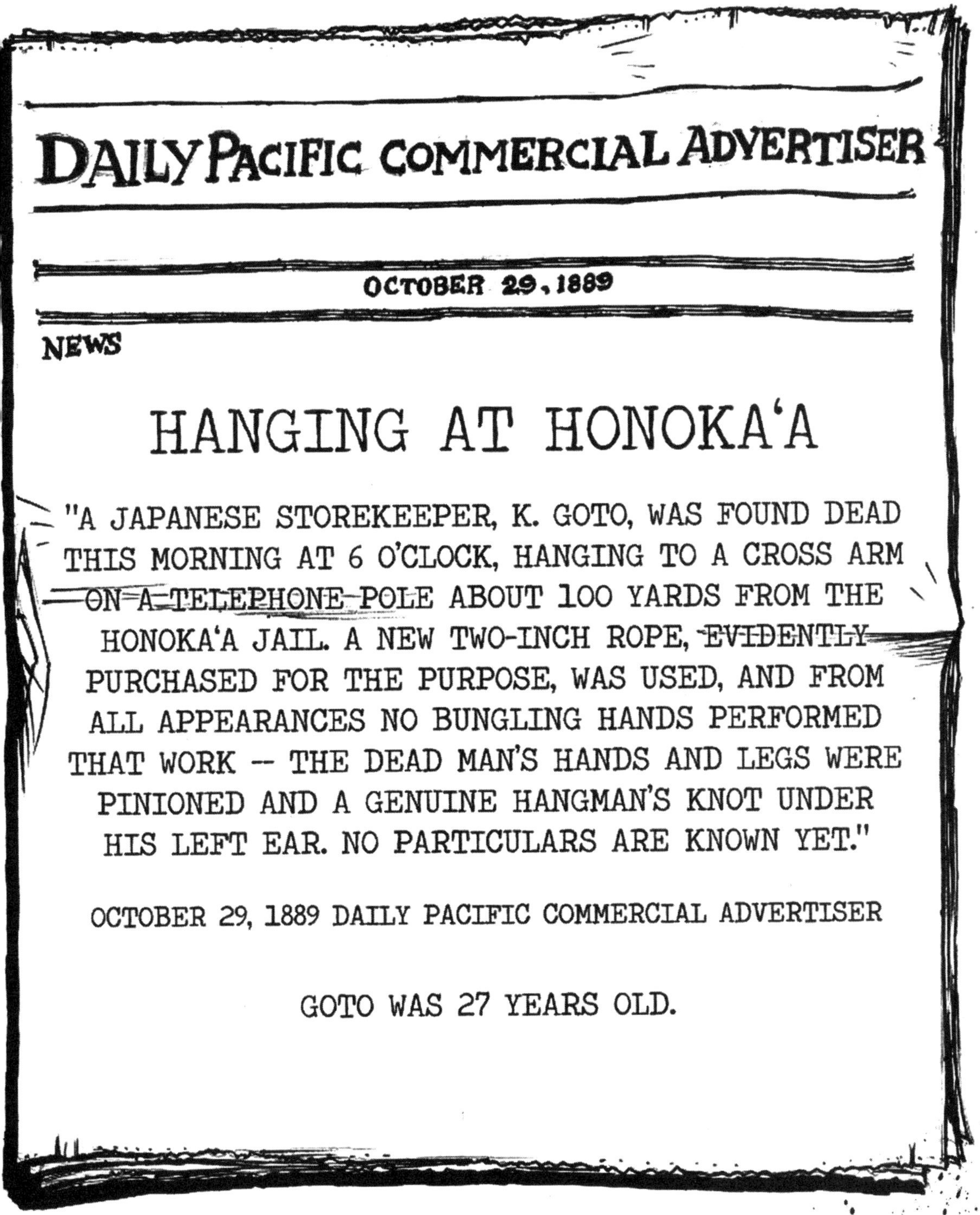

DAILY PACIFIC COMMERCIAL ADVERTISER

OCTOBER 29, 1889

NEWS

HANGING AT HONOKA'A

"A JAPANESE STOREKEEPER, K. GOTO, WAS FOUND DEAD THIS MORNING AT 6 O'CLOCK, HANGING TO A CROSS ARM ON A TELEPHONE POLE ABOUT 100 YARDS FROM THE HONOKA'A JAIL. A NEW TWO-INCH ROPE, EVIDENTLY PURCHASED FOR THE PURPOSE, WAS USED, AND FROM ALL APPEARANCES NO BUNGLING HANDS PERFORMED THAT WORK -- THE DEAD MAN'S HANDS AND LEGS WERE PINIONED AND A GENUINE HANGMAN'S KNOT UNDER HIS LEFT EAR. NO PARTICULARS ARE KNOWN YET."

OCTOBER 29, 1889 DAILY PACIFIC COMMERCIAL ADVERTISER

GOTO WAS 27 YEARS OLD.

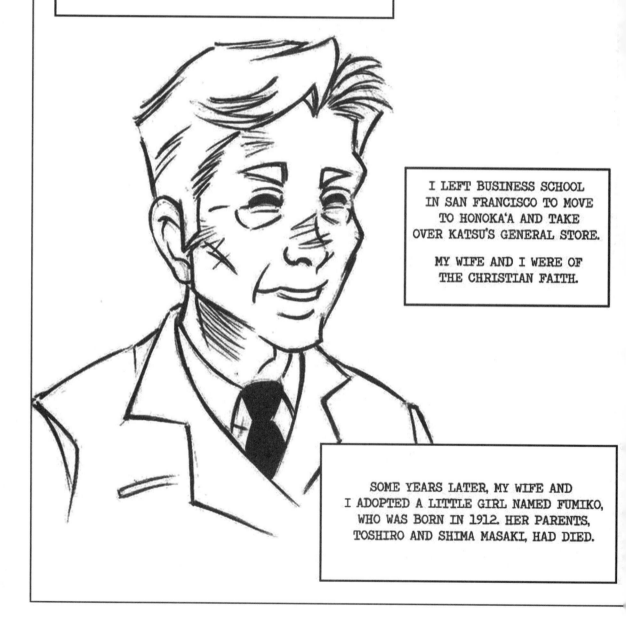

AN INVESTIGATION SPEARHEADED BY SHERIFF EDWARD G. HITCHCOCK WAS CONDUCTED. THE MEN WHO WERE INVOLVED WITH MY BROTHER'S MURDER WERE ARRESTED. A TRIAL WAS HELD SIX MONTHS LATER AND THE FOUR MEN WERE CONVICTED . . . BUT THEY ALL EVENTUALLY ESCAPED JUSTICE.

I LEFT BUSINESS SCHOOL IN SAN FRANCISCO TO MOVE TO HONOKA'A AND TAKE OVER KATSU'S GENERAL STORE.

MY WIFE AND I WERE OF THE CHRISTIAN FAITH.

SOME YEARS LATER, MY WIFE AND I ADOPTED A LITTLE GIRL NAMED FUMIKO, WHO WAS BORN IN 1912. HER PARENTS, TOSHIRO AND SHIMA MASAKI, HAD DIED.

64

EPILOGUE

Under the leadership of Sheriff Edward G. Hitchcock, along with Keigoro Katsura, an attorney acting on behalf of the Japanese Consulate General in Honolulu, an investigation was conducted and four men were eventually arrested in the murder case of Katsu Goto: William Blabon, Joseph Mills, Thomas Steele and William Watson. The trial began on May 6, 1890, approximately six months after the arrests, and it created a sensation, as it involved Mills, who was a store and restaurant owner, Honoka'a Postmaster, Honoka'a pound master, notary public, special policeman and auctioneer.

The trial ended on May 13 with the conviction of the four men on varying degrees of manslaughter. Chief Justice Francis Albert Judd sentenced Mills and Steele to nine years of imprisonment at hard labor, Blabon to five years, and Watson to four years. They were transferred to an O'ahu prison. Many felt the sentences were unjustifiably light; however, in his report to the Foreign Ministry in Japan, Viscount Chusuke Torii, vice consul of the Japanese Consulate General, said that he was satisfied with the good intentions and cooperation of the Hawaiian government in the case.

Watson would be the only one to fulfill his sentence. Steele escaped through a window and left O'ahu on a ship bound for Australia; Blabon slipped out of the prison gate and boarded a ship to San Francisco; and Mills was granted a full pardon and restoration of his civil rights by a joint session of the Executive and Advisory Councils of the provisional government of the Republic of Hawai'i.

***

Katsu Goto was a martyr and his death marked a turning point for plantation laborers in Hawai'i. As the different ethnic groups on the plantation united, which eventually led to the organization of unions, sugar plantation laborers negotiated for improved wages and working conditions. This young man, who died at the age of 27, had planted the seeds of justice and labor rights in the hard soil of Hawai'i's plantation society.

The Japanese have a saying, "Hakanai Inochi," which means our bodies are "temporary and fleeting" over the course of time. Katsu Goto made the most of his very fleeting and temporary, short four years in Hawai'i.

Fumiko (Kobayakawa) Kaya became a physician in the prefecture of Hiroshima, Japan, survived the atom bomb during World War II and became a distinguished community leader. Upon seeing a commemorative documentary on the 100th anniversary of Japanese immigration to Hawai'i in 1985 that discussed her adoptive uncle's tragic death, Kaya learned for the first time the truth about her family's history. Her adoptive father, Sekijiro Kobayakawa, had never talked about the incident. Instead of responding with anger, Kaya sought to honor the memory of her adoptive uncle Katsu Goto, who had tried to create a bridge between Japan and Hawai'i. Her goal was to create an organization that would help to improve communication and relations between the two lands.

Kaya established the Goto of Hiroshima Foundation in 1992 to provide scholarships to foster volunteer activities and research designed to contribute to and promote mutual understanding and friendship between the people of Hawai'i and Japan. From 1993 to 2007, 15 scholars were awarded the annual grants. After Kaya pssed away in 2004 at the age of 92, the Foundation evolved to become a scholarship fund, established in 2008, for American Studies students at the University of Hawai'i at Manoa.

A GOLD POCKET WATCH

Dr. Fumiko Kaya remembered her adoptive father, Sekijiro Kobayakawa, using a gold pocket watch that belonged to his brother Katsu Goto. In addition to the time, the sophisticated timepiece provided the month, day and date with separate dials. She recounts this story in her book, "Katsu Goto, the First Immigrant from Japan": "Around 1912, Mr. Miya-matsu and Sueichi Yoshigami, brothers from Hiroshima Prefecture in Japan, visited my father in Honoka'a, Hawai'i, asking for his help." The brothers were fishermen and wanted to start a business. Kobayakawa gave them over $2000 to purchase a fishing boat and supplies. However, the Yoshigamis weren't successful and later moved to Honolulu. "When my father died in Japan, the Yoshigami borthers asked at least to be allowed to build his grave and they did. To express her thanks my mother gave Sueichi Yoshigami that golden watch which my father always wore," continued Kaya. A few years before Sueichi died he asked if he could donate the watch to Bishop Museum's Hawai'i Immigrant Heritage Preservation Center in Honolulu and Kaya agreed. Kaya wrote, "When I saw it in the centennial commemorative book, 'A Pictorial History of the Japanese in Hawai'i 1885-1924,' I felt a sense of nostalgia and sensed the presence of my adoptive father."

In memory and honor of Katsu Goto and his tale of adventure, challenge, triumph and tragedy, the gold pocket watch is featured as an "Item of Interest" and on the last pages.

THE KATSU GOTO MEMORIAL COMMITTEE, HEADED BY THE LATE JITSUO KOTAKE, DEDICATED A FITTING MONUMENT TO THE PIONEER LABOR LEADER OF THE PLANTATION ERA IN HONOKA'A ON DECEMBER 10, 1994. MADE OF MATERIALS FROM HAWAI'I AND HIROSHIMA, IT IS LOCATED NEAR THE PUBLIC LIBRARY ON MAMANE STREET IN HONOKA'A, A FEW BLOCKS AWAY FROM THE LOCATION WHERE GOTO WAS LYNCHED IN 1889.

Japanese blue-tiled roof

Bronze plaque honoring Katsu Goto

Hinoki, Japanese cypress

'Ohi'a wood

Rocks from Hiroshima

Lava rock from Honoka'a

A TIME CAPSULE, FILLED WITH ARTICLES ABOUT GOTO AND PHOTOS OF HIS FAMILY MEMBERS, WAS BURIED AT THE MONUMENT. THE INSCRIPTION ON THE ROCK WALL WHERE THE TIME CAPSULE WAS BURIED READS: "PURE SPIRIT PREVAILED LIKE A BREEZE. HIS ACHIEVEMENT WAS AS NOBLE AS A SHINING STAR."

GLOSSARY OF JAPANESE WORDS

Chonan: Eldest son in the family. Inherits the family home and land is expected to care for parents.

Dekasegi: To seek work abroad; emigrate.

Hole hole bushi: Simple, plaintive, poignant songs the Japanese plantation laborers made up as they worked long hours in the cane fields under the hot, tropical sun. "Hole hole" meant to strip the cane, a task usually assigned to women. "Bushi" is the Japanese term for melody, "the blues."

Jyubako: Lacquered boxes used for serving osechi ryori.

Kadomatsu: New Year's decoration made of bamboo and pine usually placed outside at the home entrance.

Kagami mochi: Display of Japanese rice cakes.

Kanyaku Imin: "First Ship Immigrants." Katsu Kobayakawa, son of Izaemon and Sayo, learned of the government contract labor agreement between Japan and Hawai'i as an employee of the city.

Kekkon shiki (also kekkon, yomeiri, engumi): Wedding, marriage, betrothal. Most marriages in Japan during the time this graphic novel takes place were arranged by family members, friends or a matchmaker.

Osechi ryori: New Year's celebratory foods.

Oshogatsu: New Year's celebrations from December 28 to January 6. The New Year holiday is the most important event of the year for the Japanese.

Ozooni: Japanese mochi rice cakes in broth with vegetables; traditionally eaten on New Year's morning.

Sake: Japanese rice wine.

Tsukemono: Japanese pickled vegetables.

Tanomoshi: Mutual financing association.

ACKNOWLEDGEMENTS

Goto of Hiroshima Foundation

Goto of Hiroshima Hawai'i Selection Committee

Hawai'i Japan Center

Japanese Cultural Center of Hawai'i

Subaru Telescope/National Astronomical Observatory of Japan

HIDDEN ITEMS REVEALED

Did you find all 12 "treasures" from Hawai'i's Japanese American immigrant history hidden in the artwork of this graphic novel?

*tsukemono (pickles) – page 7
*geta (footwear) – page 9
*kori (wicker) suitcase – page 16
*bango "ID" tag – page 19
*cane knife – page 20
*bull whip – pages 22-23
*kau kau (lunch) pail – page 25
*kasa (paper umbrella) – page 28
*medicine – pages 30 & 34
*daikon (radish) – page 6
*oil lantern – page 45
*pocketwatch – page 56

SOURCES

"Hamakua Hero: A True Plantation Story" is a creative work based on actual events and characters according to various sources including personal interviews with Dr. Fumiko Kaya. Portions of the narration, chronology, events, characters, and dialogue may have been altered and/or adapted in the interest of storytelling. This work is not a definitive historical summary.

Another Heaven. By Eric Anderson. Dir. Justina Mattos. Perf. University of Hawaii at Hilo Performing Arts cast and crew. University of Hawaii at Hilo Performing Arts Center, Hilo. November 2005. Performance.

Another Heaven. By Eric Anderson. Dir. Sammie Choy. Perf. Kumu Kahua Theatre cast and crew. Kumu Kahua Theatre, Honolulu. May-June 2006. Performance.

Battad Ishikawa, Gwen. "Hidden Hero: Story of People's Hero, Katsu Goto, Told in Manga." *The Hawaii Herald* 30.6 (2009): 9-10. Print.

Beekman, Alan. *The Strange Case of Katsu Goto.* Honolulu: Heritage Press of Pacific, 1989. Print.

"Hamakua Hero: A True Plantation Story, Local author tells the story of Katsu Goto in a new Japanese-style graphic novel. *Big Island Weekly* 15 Dec. 2010. Print.

Iwasaki, Patsy Y. "Fumiko Kaya: Goto of Hiroshima Foundation Strengthens Ties Between Hawaii and Japan." *The Hawaii Herald* 9 Jan. 1994. Print.

Iwasaki, Patsy Y. "Goto Memorial Dedicated in Honokaa." *The Hawaii Herald* 6 Jan. 1995. Print.

Iwasaki, Patsy Y. "In Search of a Hero." *The Hawaii Herald* 6 May 1994. Print.

Iwasaki, Patsy Y. "Remembering Katsu Goto: More than a Century Later, Goto is Still Honored as a People's Hero." *The Hawaii Herald* 1 Aug. 2008. Print.

Kaya, Fumiko. *Katsu Goto, the First Immigrant from Japan.* Hiroshima, 1988. Print

Kaya, Fumiko. Personal interview. Aug. 1993

"Katsu Goto 125th Year Anniversary Service Held." *Hamakua Times.* 155 (Dec. 2010) 1+. Print

Kubota, Gaylord C. "Katsu Goto: Victim of 1889 Lynching Case, Was First Kanyaku Imin Storekeeper." *The Hawaii Herald* 6 Dec. 1985. Print

Kubota, Gaylord C. "The Lynching of Katsu Goto." *Honolulu* Nov. 1985: 76+. Print.

Kubota, Gaylord C. and Bob Dye. "The Lynching of Katsu Goto." *Hawaii Chronicles: Island History* from the pages of
     Honolulu Magazine. 1996. Print.

Pino, Krista. "Remembering Katsu Goto." *North Hawaii News* 18 June 2009. Print.

Yoneda, Karl G. "Lynching of Goto Recalls Folk Hero." *Pacific Citizen* 24 Dec. 1971. Print.